DO WHAT HE SAYS! HE'S CRAZY!!!

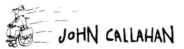 JOHN CALLAHAN

John Callahan is no ordinary cartoonist. Abandoned at birth by his mother, he was educated by Roman Catholic nuns with an emphasis on guilt and harsh discipline. He became an alcoholic by the age of 12 and was paralysed in a car accident shortly after his 21st birthday. It took six years of heavy drinking before Callahan got to realise that his problem was alcoholism and not quadriplegia. With his recovery, he returned to a childhood passion and started working hard on his cartoons. Callahan can't move all his fingers, so he draws by clutching a pen in his right hand and guiding it across the page with his left.

Now some fifteen years later, Callahan's work appears in over forty newspapers and his autobiography 'Don't worry, He won't get far on foot' has been published to critical and commercial success.

Published by Statics (London) Ltd
41 Standard Road, London NW10 6HF

Printed in England by HPH Print Ltd.
Royal London Estate, 29 North Acton Road, London NW10 6PE.

ISBN 1-873922-18-3

DO WHAT HE SAYS! HE'S CRAZY!!!

JOHN CALLAHAN

STATICS BOOKS

"I WARNED YOU NOT TO BRING THE BEAVERS!"

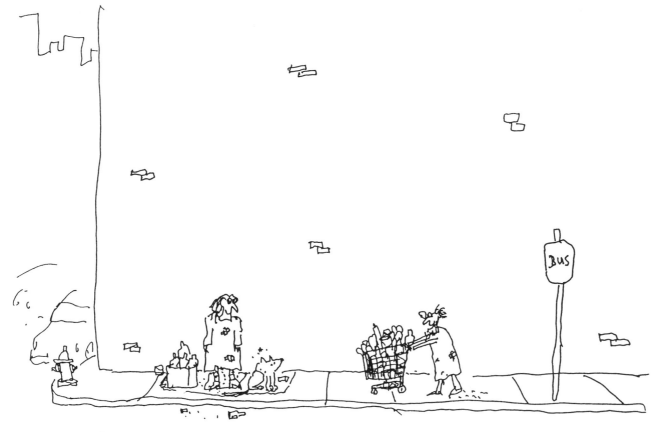

"HONEY, I'M HOME!!"

"POOR DEVIL! THAT WHALE WAS REALLY HARD ON HIM!"

"YOU SURE YOU DON'T WANT TO COME BACK TOMORROW
WHEN I'LL HAVE SOME MORE STRING?"

MOONA LISA

CALLAHAN

CALLAHAN

"THIS TOWN AIN'T ACCESSIBLE ENOUGH FOR BOTH OF US!"

CALLAHAN

THE FLATULENT NUN

1.   2.   3.

CALLAHAN

"SEE YOU MONDAY, MR. RONSON, AND BY THE WAY,
I'VE DEFINITELY CONCLUDED THAT YOU DON'T HAVE
A MULTIPLE-PERSONALITY PROBLEM!"

PICASSO SNAPS A BACKYARD PHOTO

CALLAHAN

"OKAY, EVERYBODY....ONE EYE OVER THE OTHER
AND AN EXTRA MOUTH!"

"TIE ME UP."

"IT'S GOT TO BE SILICONE!"

CALLAHAN

MADONNA WORKING IN HIGHWAY CONSTRUCTION

CALLAHAN

"NOW, CLASS, IS THIS MAN LYING OR LAYING IN THE GUTTER?"

THE POLITICALLY CORRECT CHILD   CALLAHAN

HELLO SUICIDE HOTLINE? I'VE CHANGED MY MIND!
THE CELLULAR PHONE
CALLAHAN

WILL
WORK
FOR
SHIT

CALLAHAN

"I'D LIKE TO TALK ABOUT MY ABANDONMENT ISSUES."

CALLAHAN

Let's talk about this compulsion to reach for a can of spinach every time something goes wrong.

CALLAHAN

"I'M GONNA HAVE TO GO WITH PRIZE NUMBER THREE, BOB!"

CALLAHAN

"MY CLIENT OBJECTS TO THE ENDLESS DELAYS IN THIS TRIAL. ATTORNEY FEES ALONE, HE SAYS, ARE BECOMING INCREASINGLY PAINFUL TO BEAR."

"MISS JONES, PLEASE UNPLUG THE INTERCOM!!!"

"OH, LET HIM BLOW! IT'S NOT AS BAD AS THAT
JEHOVAH'S WITNESS WOLF LAST WEEK!"

"DO WHAT HE SAYS! HE'S CRAZY!!!"

THE POPE DIGS MADONNA

CALLAHAN

"I WON'T BE NEEDING A BAG."

CALLAHAN

CALLAHAN

"HE JUST HASN'T BEEN THE SAME
SINCE HE BOTCHED THAT ELVIS JOB!"

"THE COURT SENTENCES YOU TO FIFTEEN YEARS IN THE FEDERAL PENITENTIARY WITH NO POSSIBILITY OF TV MOVIE."

CALLAHAN

"I SHOULD HAVE KNOWN YOU'D BE THE NEEDY ONE
IN THIS RELATIONSHIP!"

"I'M THINKING OF MAKING A BED AND BREAKFAST OUT OF IT."

CALLAHAN

MADONNA'S CAT

CALLAHAN

CALLAHAN

CALLAHAN

"PERRIER I PRESUME?"